MORE Improving Comprehension

for ages 7-8

A & C Black • London

Contents

Each text has three comprehension exercises to enable teachers to differentiate across the ability range.

Introduction

Following the success of the Improving Comprehension series, *More Improving Comprehension* provides a further range of interesting and exciting texts for sharing with pupils. The texts have been carefully selected to be appropriate to the age group and to cover a range of text types. The accompanying comprehension worksheets are differentiated at three levels and are designed to be used by individuals or small groups. **Notes for teachers** at the foot of each worksheet provide guidance on how to get the most from the texts and how to approach the questions on the sheet.

For monitoring and recording purposes, an **Individual Record Sheet** is provided on page 4 detailing reading and writing levels appropriate for Year 3. You may find it helpful to make indicative assessments of pupils' levels in both reading and writing by considering their responses to the comprehension exercises.

How to use the book and CD-ROM together

The book has fifteen texts, which can be projected on to a whiteboard for whole class use from the CD-ROM, or photocopied/printed for use with small groups or individuals. Sharing the text either on screen or paper provides lots of opportunities for speaking and listening, for decoding words through a phonic approach, for reading and re-reading for meaning, and for satisfaction and enjoyment in shared success.

For each text there are three comprehension worksheets at different ability levels to enable teachers to differentiate across the ability range. An animal picture at the top of the sheet indicates the level of the worksheet. The cat exercises are at the simplest level; the dog exercises are at the next level; the rabbit exercises are at the most advanced level. You may decide to give some pupils the cat worksheet and then decide, on the basis of their success, to ask them to complete the dog worksheet. A similar approach could be taken with the dog and rabbit sheets.

After reading the text with the pupils, the teacher should discuss the tasks with the children, ensuring that they understand clearly how to complete the worksheet and reminding them to answer the questions using full sentences and correct punctuation.

National Curriculum levels

The worksheets are aimed at the following ability levels:

Cat worksheets are for pupils working towards Level 2.
Dog worksheets are for pupils working at Level 2.
Rabbit worksheets are for pupils who are working confidently at Level 2 and are progressing towards Level 3.

Individual record sheet

Pupil's name: _____

Date of birth: _____

Reading Level 2
- ☐ I can show understanding when reading simple texts.
- ☐ My reading of simple texts is generally accurate.
- ☐ I can express opinions about major events or ideas in stories, poems and non-fiction.
- ☐ I can use phonic skills in reading unfamiliar words and establishing meaning.
- ☐ I can use graphic skills in reading unfamiliar words and establishing meaning.
- ☐ I can use syntactic skills in reading unfamiliar words and establishing meaning.
- ☐ I can use contextual skills in reading unfamiliar words and establishing meaning.

Reading Level 3
- ☐ I can read a range of texts fluently and accurately.
- ☐ I can read independently.
- ☐ I use strategies appropriately to establish meaning.
- ☐ In my responses to fiction I show understanding of the main points and I express preferences.
- ☐ In my responses to non-fiction I show understanding of the main points and I express preferences.
- ☐ I know the order of the alphabet.
- ☐ I use my knowledge of the alphabet to locate books and find information.

Writing Level 2
- ☐ My narrative writing communicates meaning.
- ☐ My non-narrative writing communicates meaning.
- ☐ I use appropriate and interesting vocabulary.
- ☐ I show some awareness of the reader.
- ☐ I can write a sequence of sentences to show ideas developing.
- ☐ My sentences are sometimes demarcated by capital letters and full stops.
- ☐ Usually, I can spell simple, monosyllabic words correctly or spell a phonetically plausible alternative.
- ☐ My letters are accurately formed.
- ☐ My letters are consistent in size.

Writing Level 3
- ☐ My writing is often organised, imaginative and clear.
- ☐ I use the main features of different forms of writing.
- ☐ I am beginning to adapt my writing to different readers.
- ☐ I use sequences of sentences to extend ideas logically.
- ☐ I choose words for variety and interest.
- ☐ The basic grammatical structure of my sentences is usually correct.
- ☐ My spelling is usually accurate, including that of common, polysyllabic words.
- ☐ I use punctuation accurately to mark sentences, including full stops, capital letters and question marks.
- ☐ My handwriting is joined and legible.

A visit to the cinema

Abi was very excited. For her birthday treat, Mum said she could take three friends to the cinema. Choosing who to take was really difficult but at last she had decided to take Ella, Jade and Tom.

Abi, Ella and Mum waited in the entrance to the cinema.

"Hurry up, Jade and Tom!" said Abi, looking worried. "Where are they?"

"They'll be here soon," said Mum.

Suddenly Tom arrived. "Sorry we're late," said his mum, then she kissed him goodbye. "Be a good boy, Tom!"

Then Jade's mum came in with Jade. "Hello, Sally!" she said cheerfully. "See you later, Jade."

"Right, now we're all here, who'd like some sweets?" asked Abi's mum.

"Can I have jelly babies?" asked Abi.

"I want chocolate buttons," said Ella.

"Maltesers!" said Jade.

"I want popcorn!" said Tom, excitedly.

"I'm waiting for a magic word!" said Abi's mum.

"Please!" they all said together.

"That's better," she said.

All the children went in to see the film, happily clutching their treats.

A visit to the cinema

Write a full sentence for each answer. Don't forget to start each sentence with a capital letter and to end it with a full stop.

1. Whose birthday was it?

   _____

   _____

2. What was her birthday treat?

   _____

   _____

3. Which friends were coming with her to the cinema?

   _____

   _____

4. What sweets did Ella ask for?

   _____

   _____

5. Write about a trip out you have had.

   _____

   _____

   _____

   _____

Notes for teachers

Read the passage through with the children helping them to understand the story. If you feel that they are able to do so, help them to read the story themselves using their phonic skills to decode unfamiliar words. When the pupils are confident with the text, discuss the questions on this worksheet. Encourage the children to write full sentences. The final question requires an answer that is personal to each pupil. You may wish them to write about a visit to the cinema but, if they have not been recently, you may prefer to ask them to write about a school trip or a visit to the park – what can they remember about the trip? They may need help in segmenting the words for spelling.

Andrew Brodie: More Improving Comprehension for Ages 7–8 © A&C Black, Bloomsbury Publishing 2012

A visit to the cinema

Write a full sentence for each answer.

1. Why was Abi excited?

   _____

   _____

2. Which of Abi's friends were late?

   _____

   _____

3. Who was the last person to arrive?

   _____

   _____

4. Who didn't ask for any sweets but asked for something else instead?

   _____

   _____

5. What did Abi's mum want the children to say?

   _____

   _____

6. What treat would you choose?

   _____

   _____

Notes for teachers
Read the passage through with the children helping them to understand the story. When the pupils are confident with the text, discuss the questions on this worksheet. Encourage the children to write full sentences. The final question requires an answer that is personal to each pupil. They may need help in segmenting the words for spelling.

A visit to the cinema

Write a full sentence for each answer.

1. What did Abi find difficult?

   _____

   _____

2. Why might Tom have been embarrassed when he arrived at the cinema? There may be more than one reason for his embarrassment!

   _____

   _____

   _____

3. What was Abi's mum's name and how do you know this?

   _____

   _____

4. Describe how Abi felt on her trip to the cinema. Did her feelings change in any way?

   _____

   _____

   _____

5. Describe a time when you have felt excited. What were you excited about? Were you nervous as well? What happened in the end?

   _____

   _____

   _____

Notes for teachers
Ask the children to read the passage through carefully. When the pupils are confident with the text, discuss the questions on this worksheet. Question 4 is quite demanding – can the pupils find the clues that show how Abi experiences a range of feelings? The final question requires an answer that is personal to each pupil. They may need help in segmenting the words for spelling.

   Andrew Brodie: More Improving Comprehension for Ages 7–8 © A&C Black, Bloomsbury Publishing 2012

Heathrow Airport

Heathrow Airport is located on the west side of London. It is the busiest airport in this country. Over sixty million passengers use the airport each year.

The airport has two runways. One is used for the aeroplanes to take off from while the other is used for aeroplanes to land on. Each runway is nearly four kilometres long.

More than ninety different airline companies travel to and from Heathrow. Passengers can travel to one hundred and seventy different cities in the world. More people travel to New York from Heathrow than to any other city in the world.

Aeroplanes fly from Heathrow to every continent in the world except Antarctica.

Other busy airports in the United Kingdom include Gatwick Airport, Stansted Airport, Manchester Airport, Edinburgh Airport, Belfast Airport and Cardiff Airport.

Heathrow Airport

Write a full sentence for each answer.

1. Where is Heathrow Airport?

   _____

   _____

2. How many people use the airport each year?

   _____

   _____

3. How long is each runway?

   _____

   _____

4. What is the most popular destination from Heathrow?

   _____

   _____

5. Which continent is not visited by aeroplanes from Heathrow?

   _____

   _____

6. Which airport is nearest to you?

   _____

   _____

Notes for teachers
Read the passage through to the children, helping them to understand it. If you feel that they are able to do so, encourage them to read it themselves using their phonic skills to decode unfamiliar words. The final question requires the children to consider their local airport – looking at and discussing a map may help them with this.

Heathrow Airport

Answer the questions about Heathrow Airport using full sentences.

1. Why does Heathrow have two runways?

   _____

   _____

2. How many different airlines use Heathrow Airport?

   _____

   _____

3. On which side of London is Heathrow?

   _____

   _____

4. To how many different destinations can people travel from Heathrow?

   _____

   _____

5. How many other airports are listed in the passage?

   _____

   _____

6. Have you ever been to an airport?

   _____

   _____

Notes for teachers
Read the passage through with the children, helping them to understand the main points. Talk about the passage before asking the children to attempt the questions. The final question could simply be answered with 'yes' or 'no' but point out that the instructions don't permit this! Encourage the children to elaborate on their answer – if they have been to an airport, which one was it? If they haven't been to an airport, they could state why they would or wouldn't like to.

Heathrow Airport

Answer the questions about Heathrow Airport using full sentences.

1. How many people travel through Heathrow each year?

   _____

   _____

2. To which continents could you travel from Heathrow?

   _____

   _____

   _____

3. Why do you think you cannot travel directly to Antarctica from Heathrow?

   _____

   _____

4. Why do you think Heathrow is the busiest airport in this country?

   _____

   _____

   _____

5. Which of the airports listed is in Wales?

   _____

   _____

6. Write about visiting an airport. You may like to use the back of the sheet or a separate piece of paper.

Notes for teachers
Read the passage through with the children, helping them to understand the main points. Talk about the questions, especially questions 3 and 4 where the children need to use logic to help them with their answers. The final question may be easier for those who have actually visited an airport but others could write about what they think the experience would be like, where they would like to be travelling to, who would be travelling with them, etc.

Limericks

There is a young lady from Wells

Whose feet keep on making strong smells.

She says, "It's my shoes,

Or the socks that I use."

"Take them off then!" everyone yells.

There was a thin lady from Spain

Who went for a walk in the rain.

The water came down,

Through the centre of town,

And flushed her away down the drain.

Limericks

Use full sentences to answer the questions.

1. What city was the young lady from?

   _____

   _____

2. What two words rhyme with yells?

   _____

   _____

3. What was wrong with the young lady?

   _____

   _____

4. What did everyone tell her to do?

   _____

   _____

5. What happened in the end to the lady from Spain?

   _____

   _____

6. What is the name for this type of rhyming poem?

   _____

   _____

Notes for teachers
Read the two rhymes with the children, ensuring that they understand that they are separate from each other! Point out the title of the sheet and explain that this is the name for this type of poem. Can the children identify the rhyming words? Discuss the questions and help the children to compose sentences to answer them.

Limericks

Use full sentences to answer the questions.

1. What country was the thin lady from?

    _____

    _____

2. What two words rhyme with drain?

    _____

    _____

3. What did the young lady blame for her smelly feet?

    _____

    _____

4. Which word rhymes with shoes?

    _____

    _____

5. Why did the thin lady get flushed away?

    _____

    _____

6. Which of the two poems do you prefer? Can you explain why?

    _____

    _____

Notes for teachers
Read the two rhymes with the children, ensuring that they understand that they are separate from each other! Point out the title of the sheet and explain that this is the name for this type of poem. Discuss the questions and help the children to compose sentences to answer them.

Limericks

Use full sentences to answer the questions.

1. What was the lady in Spain doing?

   _____

   _____

2. How did she get flushed away?

   _____

   _____

3. What was special about her that caused her to disappear down a drain?

   _____

   _____

4. Why did people tell the young lady to take off her shoes and socks?

   _____

   _____

5. Try writing your own limerick. Here's a first line to start you off:

   There was a young man from Neath,

   _____

   _____

   _____

   _____

Notes for teachers
Read the two rhymes with the children, ensuring that they understand that they are separate from each other! Point out the title of the sheet and explain that this is the name for this type of poem. Can the children write well-punctuated sentences when answering the questions? The final question invites them to write their own limerick – they will need to examine the rhyming structure of the two limericks to help them devise their own.

Show time Part 1

"I want everybody to sing a song in the class assembly," said Miss Norton.

"Hurray!" said Alice.

Miss Norton smiled.

"Wow, that's great!" exclaimed Jasmin.

Miss Norton smiled.

"Brilliant!" announced Joe.

Miss Norton smiled.

"Oh no!" said Will.

Miss Norton frowned. "Is that the right attitude, Will?" she asked.

"Sorry, Miss Norton," said Will.

"So what's wrong with singing in the class assembly?" asked Miss Norton.

"Everybody will be watching!" replied Will.

"That's the whole idea!" said Alice, laughing at Will.

"That's the idea I don't like," said Will quietly.

Miss Norton asked Will to come to see her. "What's the problem, Will?" she asked.

"Nothing!" said Will.

"Well, it can't be nothing if you don't want to do it," said Miss Norton kindly.

"I just don't want to do it!" insisted Will.

"There must be a reason," said Miss Norton.

"It's just that I can't sing," said Will sadly.

"I think you can," said Miss Norton, smiling at him.

"Do you?" asked Will.

Show time

Part 1

Name: _____ Date: _____

Use full sentences to answer the questions.

1. What was the name of the teacher in the story?

   _____

   _____

2. How many children were mentioned by name?

   _____

   _____

3. Which children were pleased about the class assembly?

   _____

   _____

4. Who was not pleased?

   _____

   _____

5. What was the first reason Will gave for not wanting to sing?

   _____

   _____

6. What was the final reason Will gave for not wanting to sing?

   _____

   _____

Notes for teachers
Read the passage with the children pointing out that several people are talking, as shown by the speech marks. Ask the children how they would feel if they were asked to perform in a class assembly. Which of the children in the story would they be like? Discuss the questions and help the children to compose their answers.

Show time Part 1

Use full sentences to answer the questions.

1. What did the teacher ask the children to do?

    _____

    _____

2. Who made Miss Norton smile at first?

    _____

    _____

3. Who made Miss Norton frown at first?

    _____

    _____

4. What idea did Will tell Alice that he didn't like?

    _____

    _____

5. How did Miss Norton try to help Will?

    _____

    _____

6. Would you like to sing in a class assembly?

    _____

    _____

Notes for teachers
Read the passage with the children, pointing out that several people are talking, as shown by the speech marks. Show the children the exclamation marks and talk about why they have been used. Ask the children how they would feel if they were asked to perform in a class assembly. Discuss the questions and help the children to compose their answers.

Show time
Part 1

Use full sentences to answer the questions.

1. Why did Miss Norton smile at Alice, Jasmin and Joe?

   _____

   _____

2. Why did she frown at Will?

   _____

   _____

3. Why did Alice laugh at Will?

   _____

   _____

4. How do you think Will would feel about Alice laughing at him? Would it help him?

   _____

   _____

5. Write about how you would help Will.

   _____

   _____

   _____

   _____

   _____

Notes for teachers
Ask the children how they know that people are talking in this passage. Show them the exclamation marks and talk about why they have been used. Ask the children how they would feel if they were asked to perform in a class assembly. Discuss the questions and help the children to compose their answers.

Show time Part 2

"Will, I'd like you to stay in for a minute at break time please," said Miss Norton.

Will looked worried. "Am I in trouble?" he asked.

"No, of course you're not!" she replied.

Will waited by Miss Norton's desk while everyone else went outside.

"OK, Will, let's practise some singing," said Miss Norton.

The teacher picked up her guitar and started singing while she strummed the strings. Will thought she had a lovely voice. "Right, Will, join in on the chorus," she said.

Will cleared his throat and began to sing. His voice was a bit shaky so he stopped.

Miss Norton stopped playing the guitar. "Don't worry, Will," she said. "I'm sure there's a lovely voice in there fighting to get out!"

She smiled kindly at Will so he smiled back.

"You can do it, Will," said Miss Norton. She began to play the guitar again and then she started singing. As soon as she got to the chorus, Will joined in. He sang much more loudly this time. He was very worried when Miss Norton suddenly stopped playing. He looked anxiously at her face.

"Wow!" she said. Her face was beaming.

"What?" asked Will.

"You are brilliant!" said Miss Norton. Her face still wore a wide smile.

"Am I really?" asked Will. His face was bright red.

"Honestly, Will, that's the best singing I've heard for a long time! You can go out to play now, but would you mind practising again tomorrow?"

"No, I don't mind," said Will.

So every day for the next few days, Will stayed in at break time to practise with Miss Norton.

Show time
Part 2

Use full sentences to answer the questions.

1. What did Miss Norton ask Will to do, at the start of this passage?

   _____

   _____

2. Was Will in trouble?

   _____

   _____

3. Which musical instrument did Miss Norton play?

   _____

   _____

4. Did Miss Norton like Will's singing?

   _____

   _____

5. What did Will do every day?

   _____

   _____

6. Did Will mind staying in?

   _____

   _____

Notes for teachers
Ensure that the children realize that this passage is a continuation of 'Show time – part 1'. Talk about how many people appear in this part of the story – where are the other children? Discuss the questions and help the children to compose their answers.

Show time

Part 2

Use full sentences to answer the questions.

1. Why did Will look worried at first?

   _____

   _____

2. Where did he wait while the other children went out?

   _____

   _____

3. Did Will like Miss Norton's voice? How do you know this?

   _____

   _____

4. Which part of the song did Will join in with?

   _____

   _____

5. Why did Miss Norton say "Wow!"?

   _____

   _____

6. Did Will think his singing was good?

   _____

   _____

Notes for teachers
Ensure that the children realize that this passage is a continuation of 'Show time – part 1'. Talk about how many people appear in this part of the story – where are the other children? Discuss the questions and help the children to compose their answers.

Show time

Part 2

Use full sentences to answer the questions.

1. Why did Will think he was in trouble?

   _____

   _____

2. Why did Will stop singing when he first tried the song?

   _____

   _____

3. How did Miss Norton encourage Will?

   _____

   _____

4. Why did Will suddenly look anxious again?

   _____

   _____

5. Why do you think Will's face turned bright red?

   _____

   _____

6. How do you think Will is going to get on in the class assembly?

   _____

   _____

Notes for teachers
Ensure that the children realize that this passage is a continuation of 'Show time – part 1'. Point out the speech marks – ask the children which other punctuation marks are used. Can they explain why they are used? Discuss the questions and help the children to compose their answers. The final question asks the children to predict what happens next.

Show time Part 3

At last the day of the class assembly arrived. Everyone was feeling excited. Alice, Jasmin and Joe were laughing and smiling.

Will wasn't smiling. He was shaking. His face was white. His knees felt weak.

"Are you ready, everybody?" asked Miss Norton.

All the children nodded. Miss Norton smiled at them kindly. She made Will feel better.

"Let's go to the hall then. Nice and quiet, everybody. Lead the way, Alice."

Once they were in position they all waited silently. It took ages for all the other classes to come into the hall. Will couldn't believe how many people were in the hall just to watch them!

The assembly started and everyone remembered what they had to do.

Alice remembered all the words of her poem and the whole school clapped. Alice grinned.

Jasmin remembered all of her dance and the whole school clapped. Jasmin curtseyed.

Joe remembered to read his story loudly and clearly and the whole school clapped. Joe laughed.

The class sang a song about how all the bones of the body are connected together and the whole school clapped. Everyone in the class waved.

"And now for the last part of our assembly, here's Will to sing a song," announced Miss Norton.

Will stood up nervously. The hall was silent. Two hundred and fifty pairs of eyes were looking straight at Will. He swallowed hard. Miss Norton began strumming her guitar but this time she wasn't going to sing!

Will remembered what his mum told him. He stood up straight and listened carefully to Miss Norton's music. At just the right moment he started to sing. He sang loudly. He sang clearly. He forgot all about the people watching him and he found he was enjoying the song. He was quite sorry when the song ended.

Suddenly everybody in the hall was cheering and clapping. Will looked around and was amazed to see everyone looking just at him. They were still clapping and smiling. For the first time that day Will smiled too!

Show time

Part 3

Use full sentences to answer the questions.

1. What was special about the day?

   _____

   _____

2. Which children were laughing and smiling?

   _____

   _____

3. Will wasn't smiling. What was he doing?

   _____

   _____

4. Who led the way to the hall?

   _____

   _____

5. Who performed a dance?

   _____

   _____

6. Did Will perform his song well?

   _____

   _____

Notes for teachers

Ensure that the children realize that this passage is a continuation of the two previous passages. Talk about this part of the story – where are the children at the start of this passage? Where do they go? What was it like in the hall? Who was excited? Who seemed to be worried? How did Will get on in the assembly? After a full discussion, allow the children to start answering the questions.

Show time
Part 3

Use full sentences to answer the questions.

1. How did Will feel before the assembly?

   _____

   _____

2. What made him feel better?

   _____

   _____

3. Where there many people in the hall?

   _____

   _____

4. Why did Joe laugh?

   _____

   _____

5. What was the last part of the assembly?

   _____

   _____

6. Whose advice did Will folllow?

   _____

   _____

Notes for teachers
Ensure that the children realize that this passage is a continuation of the two previous passages. Talk about this part of the story – where are the children at the start of this passage? Where do they go? What was it like in the hall? Who was excited? Who seemed to be worried? How did Will get on in the assembly? After a full discussion, allow the children to start answering the questions.

Show time

Part 3

Use full sentences to answer the questions.

1. How many people were in the hall to watch the assembly?

   _____

   _____

2. What was the class song about?

   _____

   _____

3. Write about a time when you felt really nervous or excited.

   _____

   _____

   _____

   _____

4. What was good about Will's performance?

   _____

   _____

   _____

5. Write about a time when you have been really pleased with your performance.

   _____

   _____

   _____

   _____

Notes for teachers

Ensure that the children realize that this passage is a continuation of the two previous passages. Talk about this part of the story – where are the children at the start of this passage? Where do they go? What was it like in the hall? Who was excited? Who seemed to be worried? How did Will get on in the assembly? After a full discussion, allow the children to start answering the questions. Discuss the final question, pointing out that 'performance' doesn't necessarily mean singing, dancing or acting but could refer to sport or even to the quality of work in writing, reading, maths or art.

Into the sea!

"Come on, Ebony, don't be scared!" said Mum.

"But I don't like the waves and the seaweed gets wrapped around your legs and there might be fish or crabs or eels!" said Ebony.

"Ebony, look at all those people in the water. Are they being washed away by the waves?"

"No," replied Ebony.

"Are they tangled up with seaweed?"

"No," replied Ebony.

"Are they being bitten by fish or crabs or eels?"

"No," replied Ebony.

"OK, shall we try it then?" asked Mum.

"OK, I'll be brave!" announced Ebony. She smiled at her mum and they began walking towards the sea.

Little waves were breaking gently on the sand.

"Oh!" exclaimed Ebony. She jumped back a little.

"I thought you were going to be brave," said Mum.

"I am," replied Ebony. She stepped forward again bravely.

Little bunches of green seaweed were floating on the surface of the water.

"Oh!" exclaimed Ebony. She stepped back from the water.

"It's only a little bit of seaweed," said Mum.

"We'll go round it then," said Ebony. She smiled at her mum and stepped along the sand away from the seaweed.

A small crab scuttled away right in front of Ebony's toes.

"Oh!" exclaimed Ebony. She clutched Mum's hand.

"Look how small that crab is!" said Mum.

"True!" said Ebony.

"Ready?" asked Mum.

Into the sea!

Draw a ring around the correct answer in each question.

1. Which word is nearest in meaning to 'frightened'?

   announced   wrapped   exclaimed   scared

2. What was the name of the girl in the story?

   Eliza   Ebony   Emily   Erica

Write complete sentences to answer these questions.

3. Who are the two people in this story?

   _____

   _____

4. What worried Ebony about the sea-weed?

   _____

   _____

5. What was the first thing that happened that made Ebony jump backwards?

   _____

   _____

6. Do you think that Ebony went in the sea in the end?

   _____

   _____

Notes for teachers

Read the passage through with the children ensuring that they understand the sequence of events. Encourage them to take turns in reading it through. Discuss the questions with them, pointing out how to answer the first two. Talk about the final question – can the children write more than simply a 'yes' or 'no' answer?

Into the sea!

Draw a ring around the correct answer in each question.

1. Which word is nearest in meaning to 'walked'?

    jumped   stepped   walking   hopped

2. Where were the two people?

    on a lawn   on a boat   on a promenade   on a beach

Write complete sentences to answer these questions.

3. What creatures was Ebony frightened of?

    _____

    _____

4. Was there much sea-weed in the water?

    _____

    _____

5. What creature did Ebony meet?

    _____

    _____

6. Write about a time when you went to the seaside.

    _____

    _____

Notes for teachers

Read the passage through with the children ensuring that they understand the sequence of events. Encourage them to take turns in reading it through. Discuss the questions with them, pointing out how to answer the first two. The first question needs to be considered in relation to tense. They may need extra space for answering the final question and could use the back of the sheet or a separate piece of paper.

Into the sea!

Draw a ring around the correct answer in each question.

1. Which word is nearest in meaning to 'wrapped'?

   tangled   papered   packed   decorated

2. Which word is nearest in meaning to 'washed'?

   bathed   showered   swept   bitten

Write complete sentences to answer these questions.

3. How did Mum show Ebony that the sea-weed was not a problem?

   _____

   _____

4. How did Ebony deal with the sea-weed that she saw?

   _____

   _____

5. What feature of the crab did Mum point out to Ebony?

   _____

   _____

Write a longer answer for this question.

6. What do you think happened next in this story?
   Write your answer on the back of this sheet or on a separate piece of paper.

Notes for teachers
Read the passage through with the children ensuring that they understand the sequence of events. Encourage them to take turns in reading it through. Discuss the questions with them, pointing out how to answer the first two. The first two questions need to be answered in the context given – in each case, the children need to consider which of the alternatives would make sense in this story. The final question could be answered briefly but you may wish to ask the children to extend the story.

Flight of the horse

As they climbed up into the sky the ground below them seemed to become flatter. They were racing over the tops of hills. Max held tightly to the horse's mane. He knew it wouldn't hurt because the horse had told him it wouldn't.

"Where are we going?" asked Max.

"Just wait and see!" replied the horse. The horse's voice seemed very quiet because the wind was so loud.

Max knew there was no point in asking the horse any more. He would just have to wait and see. So he looked carefully at everything he could see below him.

He could see the roofs of a few farms and cottages. He could see the tops of trees. He thought how different trees looked when you couldn't see the trunks.

Max could see hedges around fields. Some fields were green, some were yellow, some were brown and some looked white as snow. Max looked hard at those and realised that they were actually covered in huge sheets of plastic.

They crossed over a river. Max could see it for miles. It had big winding bends and some of them reflected the bright sunlight. He could see the river passing through a town in the distance.

"What town is that?" asked Max.

"Wait and see!" insisted the horse.

The buildings in the town seemed to get bigger as they flew closer. Max could see small houses and big houses. He could see churches and temples with huge spires and domes. But most importantly, in the very centre of the town was a massive castle. They seemed to be heading straight for it.

Flight of the horse

Write a full sentence for each answer.

1. What did Max hold on to?

   _____

   _____

2. What seemed very quiet?

   _____

   _____

3. What was loud?

   _____

   _____

4. What colours were the fields?

   _____

   _____

5. Why did some fields look white?

   _____

   _____

6. What building was in the middle of the town?

   _____

   _____

Notes for teachers

This passage is a continuation of the story 'Max and the horse', which appears in Improving Comprehension for ages 7–8. Read the passage through with the children, ensuring that they understand the sequence of events. Do the children realise that Max is flying on the horse – how can they tell this?
Discuss the questions with the pupils before asking them to compose their answers.

Flight of the horse

Write a full sentence for each answer.

1. Did the horse tell Max where they were going?

   _____

   _____

2. What did Max do while he was flying on the horse?

   _____

   _____

3. Why did Max think the trees looked strange?

   _____

   _____

4. Why did Max look hard at some of the fields?

   _____

   _____

5. Describe the town.

   _____

   _____

   _____

   _____

   _____

Notes for teachers

This passage is a continuation of the story 'Max and the horse', which appears in Improving Comprehension for ages 7–8. Read the passage through with the children, ensuring that they understand the sequence of events. Do the children realise that Max is flying on the horse – how can they tell this?

Discuss the questions with the pupils before asking them to compose their answers. The final question is particularly challenging but the pupils should be able to find lots of clues in the text – do they remember to mention the river?

Flight of the horse

Write a full sentence for each answer.

1. What was the landscape like where they were climbing up into the sky?

   _____

   _____

2. What two things were very special about the horse?

   _____

   _____

3. Describe what Max could see.

   _____

   _____

   _____

   _____

   _____

   _____

Write a longer answer for this question.

4. What do you think happened next in the story?
   Write your answer on the back of this sheet or on a separate piece of paper.

Notes for teachers
This passage is a continuation of the story 'Max and the horse', which appears in Improving Comprehension for ages 7–8. Read the passage through with the children, ensuring that they understand the sequence of events. Do the children realise that Max is flying on the horse – how can they tell this?
Discuss the questions with the pupils before asking them to compose their answers. However, you may wish to give the pupils no clues for the final question, encouraging them to come up with their own ideas.

The Grimm Brothers

Jakob and Wilhelm Grimm lived and worked in Germany approximately two hundred years ago.

Jakob was born in January 1785 and Wilhelm was born just over a year later. They lived in the countryside with their mother and father and their brothers and sisters. When their father died they moved into a very small house in a town.

The two brothers worked hard at school. When they were old enough they both went to university where they studied law. They became very interested in history and especially old books. They also liked to listen to stories that had never been written down.

With a good friend, whose name was August, the Grimm brothers visited towns and villages. They asked people to tell them the stories they knew. Some of the people came to their house and told them stories.

The brothers collected lots of stories and wrote them all down. When they had enough stories they put them into a book. They published their first book in 1812. It was called *Children's and Household Tales.*

The Brothers Grimm went on to collect and write down more and more stories. We know these stories as Grimms' Fairy Tales. They include famous tales such as *Sleeping Beauty, Cinderella, The Princess and the Frog* and *Snow White.*

Name: _____ Date: _____

Draw a ring around the correct answer in each question.

1. Which word is nearest in meaning to 'approximately'?

   carefully   exactly   appropriately   roughly

2. In what country did the Grimm brothers live?

   Germany   England   Scotland   Wales

Write complete sentences to answer these questions.

3. What were the first names of the two brothers?

   _____

   _____

4. What was their friend's name?

   _____

   _____

5. Why did the Brothers Grimm become famous?

   _____

   _____

6. Do you know any of the Grimms' Fairy Tales?

   _____

   _____

Notes for teachers

Read the passage through with the children ensuring that they understand that this is factual information. Encourage them to take turns in reading it through. Discuss the questions with them, pointing out how to answer the first two – help them to use their phonic skills to decode the difficult words presented as alternative answers. Talk about the final question – can the children write more than a simple 'yes' or 'no' answer?

The Grimm Brothers

Draw a ring around the correct answer in each question.

1. Who was the older of the two brothers?

    Jakob   Wilhelm   August   Otto

2. What subject did both of them study at university?

    English   German   history   law

Write complete sentences to answer these questions.

3. Why did they visit towns and villages?

    _____

    _____

4. When did they publish their first book?

    _____

    _____

5. What was their first book called when it was published?

    _____

    _____

6. Which of the Grimms' Fairy Tales have you heard of?

    _____

    _____

Notes for teachers
Read the passage through with the children ensuring that they understand that this is factual information. Encourage them to take turns in reading it through. Discuss the questions with them, pointing out how to answer the first two.

The Grimm Brothers

Draw a ring around the correct answer in each question.

1. In which year was Wilhelm born?

    1812   1786   1785   1813

2. What was the name of their first book?

    Children's and   Sleeping   Snow
    Household Tales   Beauty   Cinderella   White

Write complete sentences to answer these questions.

3. Why did the brothers move to the town when they were children?

    _____

    _____

4. Who helped the Brothers Grimm with their research?

    _____

    _____

5. How did the brothers collect the stories?

    _____

    _____

Write a longer answer for this question.

6. Write an outline of the plot of one of the Grimms' Fairy Tales.
    **Write your answer on the back of this sheet or on a separate
    piece of paper.**

Notes for teachers
Read the passage through with the children ensuring that they understand that this is factual information. Discuss the questions with them, pointing out how to answer the first two. The final question is particularly challenging. Help the children to think about the sequence of events in a story such as Cinderella. They may find it helpful to draw a picture to illustrate each of the key points in the story.

Henry's birthday present

"Happy birthday, Henry!" said his mum.

"Thanks, Mum," said Henry. "It's great being eight!"

"I know," said Mum.

"How do you know?" asked Henry.

"Well, I was eight once you know!"

"I suppose so, but I didn't think you'd remember it."

"Cheeky boy! I'm not that old!"

Henry smiled at his mum then he grinned even more when he saw a small pile of presents.

"Wow!" said Henry.

"Which one are you going to open first?" asked Mum.

"I'll open yours last," announced Henry.

"Why?" asked Mum.

"Because that's going to be the best present!" replied Henry.

"I hope you're not going to be disappointed," said Mum.

"I won't be," replied Henry confidently.

"No, I'm sure you won't be!" She looked confident too.

"Where shall I start?"

"Why don't you open Aunty Jane's present first?" smiled Mum.

"OK," said Henry, raising his eyebrows.

Henry tore at the wrapping. "I can see it!" he said. "It's pink!" he stated with a look of shock on his face.

"What is it?" asked Mum, looking worried.

Henry pulled the present out of the wrapping paper and held it up for them both to look at. Neither of them spoke. They stared at the present. It was a pink jumper with sparkly writing across the front: 'I'm a big boy now!'

Henry's birthday present

Draw a ring around the correct answer.

1. How old was Henry on his birthday?

    two   nine   seven   eight

2. Which present did Henry open first?

    the present from Uncle John   the present from Aunty Jane

    the present from Mum   the present from his sister

3. Which present did Henry think was going to be the best?

    the present from Uncle John   the present from Aunty Jane

    the present from Mum   the present from his sister

Write a full sentence for each answer.

4. What was the present from Aunty Jane?

    _____

    _____

5. What colour was the present from Aunty Jane?

    _____

    _____

Notes for teachers
Read the passage through with the children, pointing out the speech marks – do they notice that the punctuation marks such as exclamation marks and question marks are written before the closing speech marks? Discuss the questions ensuring that the children can read them. Understanding the questions is a very important aspect of comprehension.

Henry's birthday present

Draw a ring around the correct answer.

1. What did Henry say when he saw the pile of presents?

   "Thanks!"   "Wow!"   "Great!"   "Why?"

2. Which present did Henry decide to open last?

   the present from Uncle John   the present from Aunty Jane

   the present from Mum   the present from his sister

3. Which present did Mum suggest he should open first?

   the present from Uncle John   the present from Aunty Jane

   the present from Mum   the present from his sister

Write a full sentence for each answer.

4. Why did Henry look shocked?

   _____

   _____

5. What was the writing on the jumper like?

   _____

   _____

Notes for teachers
Read the passage through with the children, pointing out the speech marks – do they notice that the punctuation marks such as exclamation marks and question marks are written before the closing speech marks? Discuss the questions ensuring that the children can read them. Understanding the questions is a very important aspect of comprehension.

Henry's birthday present

Draw a ring around the correct answer.

1. What did Henry do when he saw the pile of presents?

   he opened them all   he grinned

   he shouted   he stared

Write a full sentence for each answer.

2. Why did Mum call Henry a cheeky boy?

   _____

   _____

3. Why did Henry and Mum stare at the present from Aunty Jane?

   _____

   _____

Write a longer answer for this question.

4. Write about a surprise present that you've had.

   _____

   _____

   _____

   _____

   _____

Notes for teachers

Read the passage through with the children, pointing out the speech marks – do they notice that the punctuation marks such as exclamation marks and question marks are written before the closing speech marks? Discuss the questions ensuring that the children can read them. Understanding the questions is a very important aspect of comprehension.

Andrew Brodie: More Improving Comprehension for Ages 7–8 © A&C Black, Bloomsbury Publishing 2012

Henry's thank you letter

27 West Road,
Hammerton,
Oxfordshire.
HA17 3PA

13th September

Dear Aunty Jane,

Thank you very much for your birthday present. It was a big surprise. It is a very interesting colour and the sparkling writing is very clear.

I had a very good birthday with lots of other nice presents. I got a cool game from Mum. I've played on it every day since my birthday a week ago.

It's very good being eight years old. I'm the oldest boy in my class but there's one girl older than me.

See you at Christmas.

Love,

Henry x

Henry's thank you letter

Use full sentences to answer the questions.

1. In which town does Henry live?

   _____

   _____

2. Who was Henry writing to?

   _____

   _____

3. What did Henry say in his letter about the present from Aunty Jane?

   _____

   _____

   _____

   _____

4. Was Henry the oldest child in his class?

   _____

   _____

5. When is Henry going to see Aunty Jane?

   _____

   _____

Notes for teachers
This activity should be completed after the children have worked on 'Henry's birthday present'. Help the children to read the letter that Henry sent to thank Aunty Jane for his present. Point out the features of the letter: the address, the date, the 'Dear Aunty Jane', the text itself and the closing signature. When the pupils are ready, discuss the questions with them.

Henry's thank you letter

Use full sentences to answer the questions.

1. On what date did Henry write the letter?

    _____

    _____

2. In which county does Henry live?

    _____

    _____

3. In which county, city or region do you live?

    _____

    _____

4. Henry is thanking Aunty Jane for the present she sent. What other present did Henry mention in his letter?

    _____

    _____

5. Write out your school address neatly.

    _____

    _____

    _____

    _____

    _____

    _____

Notes for teachers

This activity should be completed after the children have worked on 'Henry's birthday present'. Help the children to read the letter that Henry sent to thank Aunty Jane for his present. Point out the features of the letter: the address, the date, the 'Dear Aunty Jane', the text itself and the closing signature. When the pupils are ready, discuss the questions with them.

Henry's thank you letter

Use full sentences to answer the questions.

1. Why was Henry writing to Aunty Jane?

   _____

   _____

2. On what date was Henry's birthday?

   _____

   _____

3. How did Henry avoid telling his aunty whether he liked the present or not?

   _____

   _____

   _____

   _____

4. How can you tell that Henry really liked the present from his mum?

   _____

   _____

5. What is the postcode of Henry's house?

   _____

   _____

On the back of this sheet, or on a separate sheet of paper, write a pretend thank you letter. You can decide who you are thanking and what you are thanking them for!

Notes for teachers

This activity should be completed after the children have worked on 'Henry's birthday present'. Point out the features of the letter: the address, the date, the 'Dear Aunty Jane', the text itself and the closing signature. When the pupils are ready, discuss the questions with them. The final question invites the pupils to write their own thank you letter – this could be to thank someone for a present or for a day out or for any other special treat. Help the pupils to structure their letters correctly – use Henry's letter as a guide for this.

Swallows

Every April, swallows suddenly appear in the sky. They have returned to our country after a long flight all the way from Africa.

Swallows fly very fast. They dart through the air catching insects to eat.

Other birds that fly in a similar way are swifts and house martins. Swallows look different to swifts and house martins because they have much longer forked tails.

The upper parts of swallows are dark shiny blue. Their underparts are creamy white. They have reddy brown foreheads and chins.

Swallows usually make their nests in buildings, such as porches, garages, barns and sheds. They build their nests from mud and dry grass.

The female lays three or four eggs. The eggs are white with brown speckles. The female keeps them warm for about two weeks. When the baby birds hatch out of the eggs, both parents feed them for about three weeks. The young birds quickly learn to fly.

Swallows stay in this country until about the end of September. They fly back to Africa for the winter.

Swallows

Draw a ring around the correct answer.

1. What is the passage about?

   fish   mammals   reptiles   birds

2. What colour are the underparts of the swallow?

   reddy brown   shiny blue   creamy white   orangey brown

3. Swallows usually make their nests

   in buildings.   in trees.   in cars.   in fields.

Write full sentences to answer the questions.

4. What do swallows eat and where do they get their food?

   _____

   _____

   _____

5. Where do swallows go to in our winter time?

   _____

   _____

   _____

Notes for teachers

Read the passage through with the children, explaining that this is a non-fiction piece. Discuss the seasons with the pupils. If possible, go outside to look for swallows. Talk about the questions, ensuring that the children understand how to answer them. Question 4 is a double question and the children may need some help in interpreting what is required of them.

Swallows

Draw a ring around the correct answer.

1. From where in the world do the swallows fly to return to this country?

   Africa   Asia   America   Antarctica

2. What colour are the upper parts of the swallow?

   reddy brown   shiny blue   creamy white   orangey brown

3. Swallows usually make their nests

   from mud and reeds.   from mud and dry grass.

   from mud and sticks.   from mud and wool.

Write full sentences to answer the questions.

4. Write about the way swallows fly.

   _____

   _____

   _____

5. How can you distinguish swallows from swifts and house martins?

   _____

   _____

Notes for teachers
Read the passage through with the children, explaining that this is a non-fiction piece. Discuss the seasons with the pupils. If possible, go outside to look for swallows. Talk about the questions, ensuring that the children understand how to answer them. To answer question 4, the pupils can consider clues from the passage, which indicate speed, style and distance of flight. Help the children to read question 5 – can they find extra information from books or on the internet in order to answer this question?

Name: _____ Date: _____

Swallows

Draw a ring around the correct answer.

1. What species of bird is the passage about?

    swallows   swifts   house martins   sand martins

2. What colour is the area around the beak?

    reddy brown   shiny blue   creamy white   orangey brown

3. The young birds learn to fly approximately

    three weeks   five weeks   two weeks   four weeks

    after the eggs are laid.

Write full sentences to answer the questions.

4. Write about swallows' nests.

    _____

    _____

    _____

    _____

5. Find out about other migratory birds. Choose one that you can
    describe. Use the library or a computer to find your information.
    **Write about the bird you have chosen on a separate sheet of
    paper.**

Notes for teachers
Read the passage through with the children, explaining that this is a non-fiction piece. Discuss the seasons with the
pupils. If possible, go outside to look for swallows. Talk about the questions, ensuring that the children understand how
to answer them. To answer question 4 the pupils can consider clues from the passage, which indicate positioning and
structure of the nests, but they can also find out more information from books or the internet. Help the children to
read question 5 – do they understand the meaning of the word migratory?

Telephone message

Matty dials on the telephone. We hear a dialling tone. Answer machine replies.

Answer Machine: Welcome to the messaging service. I am sorry nobody is able to take your call at the moment. Please leave your message after the tone.

We hear a message tone.

Matty: Er … hello, it's Matty.

Answer Machine: Please leave your message.

Matty: Well, I don't know what to say really. I'm not very good with answer machines.

Answer Machine: It's quite easy really, just leave a message.

Matty: Like what?

Answer Machine: Well, you could leave your name and a number so that the person who lives here can call you back.

Matty: That's a good idea. You seem to know a lot about it.

Answer Machine: It's my job. I am an answer machine after all.

Matty: That's true. Do you enjoy your job?

Answer Machine: Yes, it's marvellous. I get to talk to so many different people and it's very good working indoors. I'm an indoors sort of machine really. Never been one for any other outdoor activity and I am sure that I would find rain or too much sun very damaging.

Matty: I'm quite an indoors type person too. I like dancing and singing.

Answer Machine: Oh, that's very nice. Look, I haven't got much time because somebody else may call. Would you like to leave your message now?

Matty: Oh, sorry, I forgot. Right, let's see. Hello, this is Matty. I am sorry you weren't in but I've had a nice time talking to your answer machine. You can call me back on 01823 7996341. Bye.

Answer Machine: Goodbye.

We hear a bleep then a dialling tone.

Telephone message

Use full sentences to answer the questions.

1. What type of passage of writing is this?

   _____

   _____

2. Who are the two characters in the script?

   _____

   _____

3. Which of the characters is not human?

   _____

   _____

4. What did the Answer Machine ask Matty to do?

   _____

   _____

5. What does Matty like to do indoors?

   _____

   _____

6. Why didn't the Answer Machine have much time?

   _____

   _____

Notes for teachers
Read the play script through with the children, pointing out features such as the italic writing indicating stage directions and non-spoken parts. Ensure that the children understand that the script consists of a conversation between a human and an answering machine. Have the children got any experience of answer machines and phone messages? Ideally, the children will act out the script in pairs. When they are confident with the script, help them to read and interpret the questions.

Telephone message

Use full sentences to answer the questions.

1. What type of passage of writing is this?

   _____

   _____

2. Who made the telephone call?

   _____

   _____

3. Why didn't Matty know what to say?

   _____

   _____

4. What did the Answer Machine suggest to Matty?

   _____

   _____

5. What does the Answer Machine like about its job?

   _____

   _____

6. How do we know that Matty liked talking to the Answer Machine?

   _____

   _____

Notes for teachers
Read the play script through with the children, pointing out features such as the italic writing indicating stage directions and non-spoken parts. Ensure that the children understand that the script consists of a conversation between a human and an answering machine. Have the children got any experience of answer machines and phone messages? Ideally, the children will act out the script in pairs. When they are confident with the script, help them to read and interpret the questions.

Telephone message

Use full sentences to answer the questions.

1. Why is some of the writing in italics?

   _____

   _____

2. What type of service does the Answer Machine provide?

   _____

   _____

3. What reason did the Answer Machine give for knowing a lot about what Matty should do?

   _____

   _____

4. Why shouldn't the Answer Machine be outdoors?

   _____

   _____

5. Do you think that Matty gave the correct information in the message?

   _____

   _____

   _____

6. Write your own short play script based on a telephone conversation.

   You could write on the back of this sheet or you could use a separate sheet of paper.

Notes for teachers

Read the play script through with the children, pointing out features such as the italic writing indicating stage directions and non-spoken parts. Ensure that the children understand that the script consists of a conversation between a human and an answering machine. Have the children got any experience of answer machines and phone messages? Ideally, the children will act out the script in pairs. When they are confident with the script, help them to read and interpret the questions.

Snowy weather

"Finally, here's the main item of the news again. Heavy snow has fallen right across the United Kingdom. The blizzards started in Kent yesterday evening. They quickly spread across London then across the North and the West.

People throughout the country woke up to find deep snow outside. Many people found it impossible to get to work. Thousands of schools have been closed.

Children and adults have made the most of the snowy weather. Lots of people have taken out their sledges for the first time this winter. Hundreds of snowmen have appeared in gardens. Some people have even made snow dogs and snow cats!

The weather forecasters are predicting more snow. Icy cold weather across Europe is going to make its way across the UK. Temperatures tonight will be at least ten degrees below zero in some parts of the country.

Wherever you are, wrap up warm. We'll be back with more news at ten o'clock. Goodbye."

Snowy weather

Use full sentences to answer the questions.

1. Who is speaking in this passage of writing?

   _____

   _____

2. What is the person telling us about?

   _____

   _____

3. Where did the snow fall?

   _____

   _____

4. What have people taken out for the first time?

   _____

   _____

5. What have people made in their gardens?

   _____

   _____

6. What is the weather forecast?

   _____

   _____

Notes for teachers
Read the passage through with the children. Do they understand that it consists of part of a television news programme and that the speaker is the news presenter? Discuss the questions with the pupils, ensuring that they understand how to answer them. They could interpret the final question to mean that they can give the current forecast for your area or to mean that they find the forecast given in the passage – either interpretation is acceptable.

Andrew Brodie: More Improving Comprehension for Ages 7–8 © A&C Black, Bloomsbury Publishing 2012

Snowy weather

Use full sentences to answer the questions.

1. What television programme is the passage taken from?

   _____

   _____

2. Where did the snow fall first?

   _____

   _____

3. Why couldn't people get to work?

   _____

   _____

4. What unusual things have people made in their gardens?

   _____

   _____

5. Where is the cold weather spreading from?

   _____

   _____

6. What is the weather like where you are today?

   _____

   _____

Notes for teachers
Read the passage through with the children. Do they understand that it consists of part of a television news programme and that the speaker is the news presenter? Discuss the questions with the pupils, ensuring that they understand how to answer them. Can they give an appropriate description to answer question 6?

Snowy weather

Use full sentences to answer the questions.

1. Describe how the snowy weather moved across the country.

   _____

   _____

   _____

   _____

2. Do we know if all the schools in the country were closed? Explain your answer

   _____

   _____

3. How do we know that some people enjoyed the snow?

   _____

   _____

4. Who might not have enjoyed the snow?

   _____

   _____

5. What is the weather like in Europe?

   _____

   _____

6. Imagine you are a television news reader. Describe today's weather where you are.

   _____

   _____

   _____

Notes for teachers
Read the passage through with the children. Do they understand that it consists of part of a television news programme and that the speaker is the news presenter? Discuss the questions with the pupils, ensuring that they understand how to answer them. Question 4 requires them to think about the snowy weather and the effect it could have on some people – the answer cannot be found in the text but instead the pupils will need to consider other people, such as the elderly or disabled. Can they give an appropriate description to answer question 6?

Building a snowman

It began to snow when Megan went to bed. It was still snowing when she woke up the next morning.

She knelt up in bed and reached up to open the curtains. The window was covered in drops of water. She felt the cold glass as she swept away the condensation. She had to rub her hands together to try to dry them.

She grabbed her clothes off the chair and pulled them into bed with her. She warmed her clothes as best she could. When she felt brave enough, Megan changed under her covers. She jumped out of bed and ran downstairs.

"School is closed because of the snow!" announced Mum.

"I guessed it would be," replied Megan. "That's why I didn't put on my uniform."

"Clever you!" said Mum.

Megan pulled on her coat, hat, gloves and wellies.

"Aren't you going to have any breakfast?" asked Mum.

"Later!" called Megan, as she stepped out into the snow.

She was the first person to go outside so the whole garden was smooth and white. She took a few steps then picked up some snow to make a snowball. Scooping up more snow, she was able to make the snowball fatter. Then she rolled it along the ground. More and more snow was sticking to the snowball. At last, the ball was big enough to be the body of a snowman.

Megan started a fresh snowball and made it big enough to be the snowman's head. She lifted the head on top of the body.

Now the snowman needed some eyes and a nose and mouth. Some stones from the path would be perfect. Megan went back towards the house and dug through the snow.

After putting the stones in place, Megan stepped back and looked at the snowman. She took off her own hat and scarf and dressed the snowman carefully.

"Now you've got a pink hat and scarf you can be a snow *girl* if you want to!" she said.

Building a snowman

Use full sentences to answer the questions.

1. What is the name of the girl in the story?

   _____

   _____

2. Where did she get dressed?

   _____

   _____

3. Why is the school closed?

   _____

   _____

4. What outdoor clothes did Megan put on when she went outside?

   _____

   _____

5. What did Megan use to make the eyes, nose and mouth?

   _____

   _____

6. What colour were Megan's hat and scarf?

   _____

   _____

Notes for teachers
Read the passage through with the children, ensuring that they understand the sequence of events. Encourage them to take turns to read it out loud. When they are confident with the story, discuss the questions with them. Help them to compose full sentences to answer the questions; for example, an appropriate answer to question 1 could be The girl in the story is called Megan.

 Andrew Brodie: More Improving Comprehension for Ages 7–8 © A&C Black, Bloomsbury Publishing 2012

Building a snowman

Use full sentences to answer the questions.

1. How did Megan's hands get wet?

   _____

   _____

2. Why didn't Megan put on her school uniform?

   _____

   _____

3. Why was the garden smooth and white?

   _____

   _____

4. Why would the garden not be so smooth and white once Megan had built the snowman?

   _____

   _____

5. What did Megan use the stones for?

   _____

   _____

6. What outdoor clothes did Megan have on after she had finished making the snowman?

   _____

   _____

Notes for teachers
Read the passage through with the children, ensuring that they understand the sequence of events. When they are confident with the story, discuss the questions with them. Help them to compose full sentences to answer the questions. Can they find appropriate answers to questions 4 and 6 where they will need to think logically in relation to the information they can find in the text?

Building a snowman

Name: _____ Date: _____

Use full sentences to answer the questions.

1. For how long was it snowing?

   _____

   _____

2. What was on the window?

   _____

   _____

3. Why did Mum think Megan was clever?

   _____

   _____

4. Why do you think Megan didn't have her breakfast straight away?

   _____

   _____

5. Describe how you would make a snowman.

   _____

   _____

   _____

   _____

   _____

Notes for teachers

Read the passage through with the children, ensuring that they understand the sequence of events. When they are confident with the story, discuss the questions with them. Help them to compose full sentences to answer the questions. Can they find an appropriate answer to question 1 where they will need to think logically in relation to the information they can find in the text? For the final question the pupils could extract information from the text or they could think of their own methods.

Andrew Brodie: More Improving Comprehension for Ages 7–8 © A&C Black, Bloomsbury Publishing 2012